Modern Calligraphy

AN INTENSIVE PRACTICE WORKBOOK

KESTREL MONTES

inkmethis.com

Published by inkmethis

inkmethis.com | @inkmethis

Santa Rosa, CA 95404 | First printing, 2018

Paperback edition 978-1-7327505-0-0

Hardback edition 978-1-7327505-2-4

Spanish edition 978-1-7327505-1-7

Printed in the United States of America.

Cover design: Kestrel Montes

All photos unless otherwise noted: Kestrel Montes

Editing: Kestrel Montes

Technical support: Betsy Miller

Proofing: Jan Davis and Joanna Krupnick

Special note of gratitude to:

Francisco for tirelessly supporting
all my crazy ideas and workaholic
tendencies. I love you and this
amazing life we have built together!

My Kids who make me so proud and
give me the motivation to better myself.

My Parents for believing in me and
encouraging me to follow my path.

Betsy for demystifying the land
of publishing.

Contents

1.

Getting Started

I am excited to join you on your calligraphy journey! Whether you are hoping to pen your own wedding invitations, create a booming calligraphy business, or simply find a new hobby, this book will launch you into a successful journey with calligraphy.

Having been a career educator before becoming a professional calligrapher, teaching calligraphy is a blend of my two lives. It's thrilling to see other people find as much joy in this not-lost art as I have and I hope you will share your work with me on Instagram.

When I first started calligraphy, I was simply trying to copy what I saw online. I watched the gorgeous videos on Instagram and tried to do it myself. That worked minimally but I struggled and got frustrated. It was definitely harder than it appeared! Sometimes I couldn't get the nib to even write, my paper would bleed and the letters didn't look anything like what I saw or imagined. I wondered how people were doing it and almost gave up more than once!

Determined to discover the hidden tricks, I kept digging through the Internet, messaging people on Instagram with questions (often times not getting responses) and buying books. Little by little, I figured it out!

My goal in this chapter is to offer a summary of the tips and the technical background information that I spent the first year or more piecing together from random sources and figuring out through trial and error. I wanted to put it all in one book for you!

If you are brand new to all of this, I encourage you to read through this chapter and simply let as much sink in as possible. As you practice, refer back to solidify more aspects of the technical side. If you have been practicing a while, your writing will undoubtedly improve from further understanding of the tools and techniques.

My ultimate desire is to help you find much more enjoyment than frustration from this beautiful art. And I'd love to see your progress!! Please share on Instagram by tagging me @inkmethis and using #learnwithkestrel.

HOW TO PRACTICE

Like an athlete in training, the goal with calligraphy practice is to build muscle memory. And like an athlete, you want your practice to be focused. For that reason, my philosophy is that you should learn one script style at a time. Instead of trying to be good at everything, I believe it is more valuable to aim for quality over quantity of styles. Therefore this book will provide intensive practice opportunities using one lettering style. After finishing this book, you will be ready to tackle a new style. Each style you learn creates a stronger foundation for learning subsequent styles.

As you practice, be mindful of your arm position, the holder's position and the position of your paper. Do not rush. Again, like an athlete in training, sloppy or rushed practice leads to sloppy muscle memory. Go slowly and focus on each stroke. If you find yourself getting bored and rushing through, that means you just aren't in the mood and it's time to walk away for a while.

In calligraphy, the ultimate goal is to have consistency; consistency in angle, in spacing, in stroke pressure (which determines how thick/bold the lines are) and consistency in size. Regardless of the style, from traditional to modern, this consistency is what will make your writing look polished and visually appealing. As your practice progresses, examine your writing with these elements in mind. Study your areas of weakness and the focus on them at your next sitting.

Frequent short practice sessions will lead to greater improvement than occasional marathon sessions. Instead of practicing for four hours on the weekend, try to practice for

half an hour four times a week. I find that I am more likely to practice if I have my basic supplies (one holder with nib, ink and paper) in a location central to where my family spends evening time. While my husband watches TV, I will sit nearby and practice calligraphy.

USING EXEMPLARS

An exemplar is a single piece of paper that shows you the whole alphabet in a particular lettering style. When doing calligraphy, it is very helpful to have an exemplar on the table nearby to quickly glance at for reference. This is especially true when you are first starting or after you learn multiple lettering styles (even professionals use exemplars). We all need a reminder sometimes of "just how does a G go in this script again?"

WRITING SPEED

When I first started trying to teach myself calligraphy, it was in the days when Instagram only allowed for 15 seconds video posts. People would use apps like Hyperspeed to speed up their videos in order to crunch them into 15 seconds. While I knew the videos were sped up, I was under the impression that people wrote calligraphy at normal cursive writing speed. A handful of months into practicing, I finally saw my first real time video. What a mind-blowing revelation! It changed my writing instantly. In calligraphy, we are not really writing in the standard sense of the word. We are slowly (and I mean slooooowly!!) drawing each stroke to form letters. Because of my experience, I am very conscious to only post real time videos on social media. If you have not seen real time calligraphy, make sure to watch videos to see just how slowly one writes.

USING SLANT LINES

In calligraphy, slant lines are used as visual guides to help keep writing at a consistent angle. Similar to how the horizontal rule lines on paper act as visual guides to keep your letters the same height, slant lines act as visual guides to help you keep your letters angled to the same degree. In Copperplate script, one of the most popular styles of pointed pen calligraphy, a 55° letter angle is often used while Spencerian, another popular traditional hand, is commonly at a 52° angle. With modern scripts, you have the liberty of deciding at which angle you want to write. The angle of the script can be decided based on the tone of the piece. For example, a more upright script may have a more juvenile or playful mood while a more slanted writing angle often times looks more sophisticated and elegant. However, no matter the angle, it should be consistent throughout the writing of a single work. If some of the letters are upright and some are more slanted, the writing will look less polished and even messy. Slant consistency is difficult to achieve without visual assistance so we use paper with slant guides or draw them on.

LETTER ANATOMY

- *Ascender height:* The height of the strokes that reach above the mean line such as the upper part of the h, l, and k.

- *X height:* The height of the body of the lowercase vowels and letters like n, m, x.

- **Descender height:** The height of the strokes that drop below the baseline such as the hanging part of the g, j, and q.

- **Meanline:** The line to which the body of the non-ascending letters reach. Also referred to as the waistline.

- **Baseline:** The line on which the letters "sit" (in this example, the base of the l and the second t dip below the baseline to create visual interest. This is called an oscillating baseline or is also referred to as bounce.

- **Ligature:** Two letters that are joined together to form a single character (here, there is a single crossbar joining the two t's as if they were one letter).

- **Slant guide lines:** Visual references to assist in maintaining consistent stroke angle.

- **X height ratio:** The x height ratio is the proportion between the x height and the ascender/descender height. The example shows a 1:1:1 ratio, where all three are the same size. The units are listed in order of ascender, x height, descender. Also common in calligraphy are 2:1:2 (ascenders and descenders are 2 times the size of the x height) and 3:2:3 ratios (ascenders and descenders are one and a half times the size of the x height).

WHAT'S A FONT

I can't help it! I have to add this part! People often make the mistake of using the term "font" when referring to handwritten calligraphy. Please use proper terminology and don't be one of those people who comments on Instagram, "Ooh. That's a pretty font!"

A font is digital and is installed on a computer for typing. If talking about hand lettering/calligraphy, we do not refer to different scripts as "fonts" but rather, as "hands" or "scripts" or "styles" because we are not computers. However, I do make fonts from my scripts (through a lengthy process of scanning, vectorizing and then programming Open Type font files for install).

PROPER NIB ANGLE

The nib should be at about a 45° angle to the paper. The more upright the nib, the more you are writing on the point of the nib which creates the finest hairlines. Experiment some with the angle of the nib to the paper. Too upright will cause snagging on the upstrokes. Too horizontal to the paper will cause bold hairlines or pools of ink. Start with the nib more perpendicular to the paper and keep lowering it gradually until you find the most upright angle at which you can achieve upstrokes without snagging.

PROPER GRIP

While many calligraphy manuals will dictate a specific grip, I am of the belief that your writing will be better if you use the grip that is most comfortable and natural to you. I know I've been holding a pen/pencil the same way for over 40 years (I rest it on my ring finger). For me to change my grip now would take too much mental and physical energy away from my actual writing.

That said, there definitely is a way the holder should be rotated in your hand. Unlike pencils or ballpoint pens, there is a top and a bottom to nibs. When writing, the nib itself should be in line with the slant of your writing. This is important for ink flow. When pulling down on the nib (writing in a downward motion called a "down stroke"), the tines should be pulled apart evenly. This will both create a smoother writing experience and make your nib last longer as the tines won't be forced to open at an angle or cross.

The rotation of the holder is by far the most common mistake I see on Instagram and what I spend most time correcting during workshops. To align the nib to the writing slant, simply rotate the holder in your hand. While gripping the holder in your writing hand and without letting go of it, use your non-writing hand to spin the holder until the nib is at the same angle as the slant of the writing.

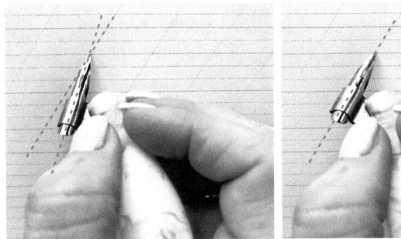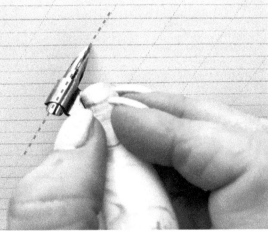

Left photo (incorrect): Nib is not aligned with writing slant (holder needs to be rotated clockwise)
Right photo (correct): Nib and writing slant are aligned (without changing grip or hand position)

PAPER PLACEMENT & WRITING ZONE

I write with my paper at or near a 90° angle with the top facing my left. It is very difficult to write with the paper straight upright as it requires your wrist to be twisted upward. My goal in finding the optimal paper rotation is to find the spot where a simple up and down finger motion actually creates strokes at the desired writing angle following the slant guides of my paper. This way, instead of trying to write at a slant, I am actually writing in straight finger movements and the paper rotation is doing the work for me. Try rotating your paper similar to what I show here. I assure you it will make a world of difference.

On my desk is a leather writing pad (blotter). The leather surface is just enough padding to reduce friction and allow the nib to flow more freely on the paper. If you do not have a blotter, you can use a stack of paper. I have a jar of water for rinsing, ink in a jar with a

mouth wide enough for easy dipping, and a paper towel for drying my nib after rinsing. Everything I need is positioned for easy access.

With my left (non-writing) hand, I gently hold the edge of the paper. When I get about half way across the page, I shift the paper closer to my body. It is important to stay in your "writing zone" and to move the paper as needed. Your writing zone is an area roughly the size and directly below your face when looking down at the paper.

If we reach far away from our body, the rotation of our arm changes which impacts the angle of our writing. Instead of compensating for this by twisting our wrist, it is best to keep your arms in position and move the paper. Similarly, if I write to the bottom of the page without moving the paper, my arm will no longer be resting on the table. The meat of my forearm should stay resting on the table to give me stability. For longer strokes such as a long t crossbar, I can roll my arm on this meaty part of my forearm to create a smoother stroke than if my arm is floating.

LEFTY LETTERING

Many left-handers wonder if they can do calligraphy. The answer is a resounding YES!! There are some brilliantly talented left-handed calligraphers that create swoon-worthy script.

While I'm not a left-handed calligrapher, I can share the observations I've made while teaching left-handed students:

- If you write without hooking your hand over, that will make calligraphy easier. As ink takes a while to dry, an over-hook grip will make it difficult to avoid smearing.

- Rotate your paper horizontally so the top is pointing to your right. This will position you to write from the top of the page to the bottom of the page while moving your hand towards your body and keeping your arm at a comfortable angle.

- Try different holders. Because of all the unique left-handed grips, there is no one holder that works best. Some lefties prefer a right-handed oblique, some a left-handed oblique (the flange is inserted on the opposite side of the holder) and some prefer a straight holder as shown here. I would recommend you buy the cheapest holder you can find of all three styles and experiment some for yourself before investing in a nicer quality holder.

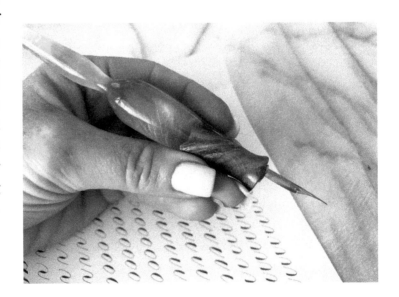

NIB ANATOMY

1. ***Tip:*** The tip of the nib should come together as a point with no gap.

2. ***Tines:*** The two tines should be so tight when in resting position that they appear to be a single piece of metal. During use, the tines spread with pressure to create thicker lines.

3. ***Vent hole or eye:*** The hole in the center of the nib allows for flexibility of the tines as well as creates an ink reservoir through the surface tension properties of liquids. Some brands use fancy shapes for the eye while others keep it simple.

4. ***Shoulder slits:*** Additional cuts in the metal on the sides of the nib create flexibility and prevent binding or cracking of the metal as it bends with use.

5. ***Shaft:*** The body/base of the nib that is inserted into the flange. This is also where the brand/model is stamped for brand identification.

NIB VARIETY

There are hundreds of nibs on the market. While your local art store may have some pointed pen nibs, most people need to buy them online. I have some of the popular nibs in my shop and there are many more on sites such as Paper and Ink Arts.

It should be noted that nibs are also called "pens." Thus, when someone speaks correctly of a calligraphy pen, they are referring to the nib not the holder.

- ***Vintage vs modern:*** I have successfully avoided the temptation of buying vintage nibs. They can be quite pricey and difficult to find so I prefer not to risk becoming attached. Modern nibs are well constructed and most are under a couple of dollars each. This allows me to keep a healthy supply and replace without concern when I notice the writing quality falter.

- ***Sharpness:*** The sharpness of the nib tip is what determines the fineness of the hairlines created when writing in an upstroke (upward motion). For example, the Leonardt Principal EF is sharper than the Brause Steno and therefore creates a finer hairline. Sharper nibs can have a greater tendency to snag the paper.

- *Flexibility:* The flexibility of the nib determines the thickness of the shaded strokes (the bolder strokes created when writing in a downward motion). More flexible nibs are trickier to use as you need to have better hand control to keep the pressure consistent otherwise some of your shades will be bolder than others. To test the flexibility of a nib, push the tines apart against your finger. You will notice the difference between two nibs when comparing. For example, the Brause Rose will spread much easier than the Nikko G and therefore would be called "more flexible."

- *Size:* The size of the nib will mostly determine the amount of ink it holds, thus, how often you need to dip. For example, the BrauseEF66 holds much less ink than the Brause Steno 361.

- *Pointed vs. Broad Edge:* For this type of calligraphy as well as traditional hands like Copperplate and Spencerian, make sure you purchase pointed nibs. Broad edge nibs are the ones that are flat at the tip like a chisel and are used in other forms of calligraphy such as uncial and blackletter.

BEST PRACTICE NIBS

When beginning, it's recommended to use a less flexible nib as they are easier to control. Some great nibs for beginners (and loved by experts alike) are the Tachikawa G, Nikko G, Zebra G, Hiro 40, or the Brause Steno 361. One of my personal favorites is the Tachikawa G which I include with each of our handmade holders and use in all my workshops. However, there is no one best nib. If you have the opportunity to try a few, you can see which works best for you. Over time and with different inks/papers, you may find that different nibs work better for you (so don't toss them even if you don't like them at the moment).

NIB & FLANGE ALIGNMENT

When inserting the nib into the flange, the tip of the nib should line up with the center axis of the holder. If the holder is well-constructed with the flange secured at an angle specific to the individual holder's dimensions, the nib will be well-positioned. By "well-positioned," I mean that the nib is inserted far enough into the flange to hold it securely without wiggling and yet enough of the shank is exposed to allow for dipping past the eye without getting ink on the flange. There is a huge range of holder prices depending on their construct but any holder with proper geometry is a good holder. The rest is simply aesthetics and depends on what you find comfortable to hold (for example, inkmethis holders are a little thicker because that's what I find more comfortable).

You do not need to wait until you are an expert to use an oblique holder. I teach all beginning students with an oblique holder. While there are some professional calligraphers who prefer a straight holder, most agree that the angle of the oblique flange greatly improves their writing and assists in creating the slant that is desired in most script styles without torquing the hand.

While oblique holders do look intimidating, as long as you hold them correctly (see Proper Grip section), you will be surprised to find that they are no more difficult to write with.

NIB PREPARATION & CARE

There are many techniques for prepping new nibs. Ultimately, the nib needs to be clean so the ink will stick to it. Storage oils used to protect new nibs and even just finger oil from touching the nib will cause the ink to roll off. A few easy ways to clean a nib include: Windex, rubbing alcohol, Clorox wipes, and saliva. Remember not to touch the nib after cleaning (finger oils!) so it's best to clean the nib while already inserted in the holder. If you need to adjust the nib in the holder after cleaning, grab it with a paper towel to avoid touching it.

During writing, to keep ink from drying on the nib and blocking flow, periodically rinse the nib in water as a painter would rinse their brush (however, only submerse the nib and not the flange or holder itself). Keep paper towels on hand for drying the nib. Upon finishing your session always clean and dry nibs before storage.

Left photo: The ink is not sticking well to the nib. There is only a small amount of ink at the tip. The oils on the nib are causing the ink to bead and roll off.
Right photo: After cleaning the nib with Windex, the ink is sticking and the nib is well-loaded with ink past the eye but not on the flange.

NIB LONGEVITY

With walnut ink and smooth paper, you may use the same nib for months as long as the tines do not get bent in storage or during cleaning. However, if you use a highly acidic ink such as iron gal ink or you write on an abrasive surface such as stone, the nib may last just one sitting. If the tines no longer meet at a perfect point or the nib has rusted to the point of obstructing ink flow, it's time to toss it. The nice part about modern nibs is that they are fairly inexpensive. While you want to take care of them as much as possible, they are ultimately rather disposable. Don't torture yourself trying to use a nib that no longer works well. It's best to buy nibs in packs so you have a handful and not just one.

DIPPING IN INK

When dipping the nib in ink, dip past the eye of the nib. This hole in the nib allows it to hold more ink due to the surface tension properties of liquids. After dipping, gently shake the holder or touch the tip of the nib to the rim of the jar to remove any excess ink that may cause a drip.

Once you see the eye pop open, it will be your signal that you will need to dip soon. Find a good place between strokes to dip. If the ink is not sticking to the underside of the nib, clean it again. Observe how more ink will stick to the nib the cleaner it is. Be careful not to dip the flange into the ink or it will drip onto your paper. If you accidentally dip too far, simply remove the nib and tap the ink out of the flange on a paper towel.

BEST PRACTICE INKS

While there are tons of fun colors and all sorts of gorgeous shimmery metallics, not all inks are equally user friendly. When practicing and with students, I believe the focus of attention is best kept on the letter forms and not on the ink itself. Therefore, I recommend sticking with walnut ink or sumi ink (which comes in black or vermilion) for practicing.

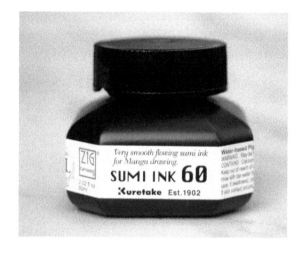

Once you are comfortable and confident writing with the pointed pen, then have fun venturing into the expansive land of colored inks! I like the iridescent colored calligraphy inks by Dr. Ph Martin and there is a whole world of colors to be made with gouaches and Pearl Ex pigment powders.

Acrylic inks will dry on non-porous or glossy substrates such as agate and highly coated papers. Additionally, acrylic inks add the benefit of permanency which can be especially helpful with envelopes when there is concern of harsh weather. The warning I will give is that acrylic inks can be pesky and have a high tendency to roll off your nib creating a blob of ink on the paper. The best acrylic inks I've found are those by Ziller.

But, again, I highly recommend sticking to walnut and sumi inks until you develop a basic proficiency. The last thing you want is to get frustrated by difficult inks when you are trying to learn a new skill or script. I still normally use sumi or walnut ink for practice so that all my mental attention is focused on my practicing goal for that sitting.

INK MIXING

Most colored and metallic inks will separate as they sit causing the pigment and shimmer to sink to the bottom. You can either leave a small stir stick in the jar and mix before each dip or you can use an electric ink mixer. There are various mixers on the market depending on your needs. The inkmethis magnetic stirrer is corded while others are battery powered.

When using powdered pigments such as Pearl Ex the most important thing you need to know is to use gum arabic. Gum arabic is made from acacia tree sap and acts as the binder to hold the pigment to the paper. It comes in both dried and liquid forms. To use Pearl Ex pigment powders, mix equal parts of pigment and water then add half part gum arabic (ex. 1 tsp pigment, 1 tsp water, 1/2 tsp gum arabic). If you only add water, your writing will brush off the page after the ink dries. A lot of ink mixing is experimental, so adjust as needed.

If your hairlines are skipping, most likely the ink is too thick and needs more water. If the ink rubs off when dry, add more gum arabic.

When using gouache (pronounce gwash), simply thin with water by adding a little at a time until you achieve good ink flow. Gouache is already gum arabic based, but you may add a little more to make the ink glossier. Gum arabic can also be added to white ink to reduce some of the chalkiness and to help prevent cracking (especially on envelopes that will pass through the postage readers).

Photo: Magnetic ink stirrer from inkmethis.com.

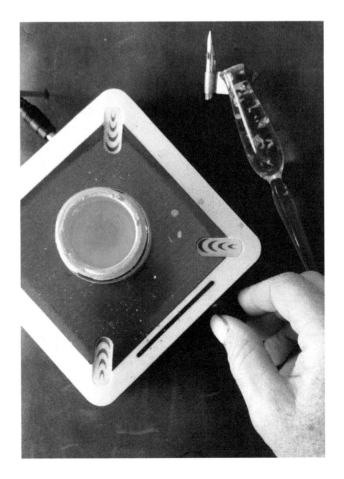

BEST PRACTICE PAPER

The best paper for calligraphy practice is a low absorbent and smooth paper. The low absorbency will eliminate ink bleed and the smoothness will allow the nib to glide without catching. A few examples of smooth papers I recommend for practice: HP Premium 32, Rhodia pads, and Claire Fontaine pads. If you are printing practice pages, make sure to put good paper in the printer. Regular copy paper will bleed and snag the nib causing splatters and much frustration.

When you are ready to create a piece for gifting or framing, watercolor papers work well for calligraphy as they are designed to handle the wetness of paint (for us, it will be ink). Cold pressed watercolor papers have more texture which is beautiful but trickier to write on while hot pressed watercolor papers are smoother. Watercolor paper can be purchased online or at your local art store.

Photo: Ziller ink on cold pressed watercolor paper.

SUPPLY LISTS

First, let me say that I do not believe you need to spend a lot money on hoards of supplies to create gorgeous calligraphy works. In fact, I tend to be quite simple in my personal collection of materials and supplies. However, the options offered are extensive and a bit overwhelming when just starting out and learning. Hopefully this list gets you pointed in the right direction. Also, on my website, inkmethis.com, I try to keep an updated list of Amazon links to the brands I personally purchase and like. I am not endorsed in any way by the listed brands, I simply have the links there as an easy way to answer recommendation questions.

The essentials:

- Properly constructed nib holder*
- Sampling of pointed pen nibs
- Sumi ink or walnut ink
- Smooth calligraphy quality paper
- Guide sheets (free downloads on inkmethis.com)

Photo: Complete calligraphy starter set curated and offered on inkmethis.com.

The next level:

- White ink
- Gum arabic
- Colored or metallic inks
- Magnetic ink stirrer*
- Leather or clear desk pad/blotter*

For finished composition pieces:

- Thick calligraphy quality paper (such as watercolor paper)
- Drying rack for holding papers with wet ink*
- Laser level
- Clear plastic ruler
- Light pad (for placing final draft over guide sheet or rough draft)
- Phantom Writer (creates visual illusion of guide lines on your paper)
- Kneaded eraser

Specialty items made and offered on inkmethis.com

Photo: My typical desk setup for a project is light pad with clear blotter and guide sheet, rinse water, ink, paper towels, and drying rack.

2.

The Basic Strokes

Yayyy!! We are ready to actually put some ink on the paper!!

In this section, you will learn what are called the "basic strokes" of calligraphy. These strokes are the foundation of almost all lowercase letters. Therefore, although they may seem silly, they are extremely important. I still, to this day, practice the basic strokes as warm-up before getting started on full words.

As you practice, be mindful of every move. Do not rush. Like an athlete in training, your goal is to build muscle memory. And like an athlete, you want to practice using correct form. Sloppy or rushed practice leads to sloppy muscle memory. Go slowly and focus on each stroke. If you find yourself getting bored and rushing through (it happens to me too when I'm just not in the mood), that means it's time to walk away for a while.

In calligraphy, the ultimate goal is to have consistency: consistency in angle, in spacing, in stroke pressure (which determines how thick/bold the lines are), and consistency in size. Regardless of the style, from traditional to modern, this consistency is what will make your writing look polished and visually appealing.

At the top of the page, I have demonstrated the stroke breakdown and direction. Start each stroke at the open circle. After tracing multiple lines, you will trace a few and write independently.

Reminders:
- Move your paper to stay in your "writing zone"
- Dip between strokes after the eye "pops"
- Rinse nib periodically
- Check the rotation of the holder in your hand frequently
- Go slowly
- This is fun!!!

This section is at 6.5mm x height with 55° degree slant lines.

FULL PRESSURE STROKE (SHADES)

Start at the top and draw a downward stroke applying slight pressure to the nib. Do not force the nib open as it will dig into the paper. Gentle pressure will spread the tines to create a bold line.

GOALS

Apply consistent pressure to create the same stroke thickness all the way down. Try to space strokes evenly and follow the slant of the guidelines.

UPSTROKE (HAIRLINES)

Start at the bottom and draw an upward stroke without applying any pressure to the nib. The stroke gently curves at the base and then the slant meets the guidelines

GOALS

Touch the paper as gently as possible to create a delicate line. Aim for equal spacing and slant.

UNDERTURN

Start at the mean line, use pressure in a downward motion transitioning to an upstroke using no pressure.

GOALS

Release pressure gradually starting about half way down the pressure stroke to create gradual taper in stroke width. The bottom curve should be a no pressure hairline. Aim for equal spacing, equal width and slant that follows the guidelines

OVERTURN

Start at the base line, use no pressure in upward motion transitioning to downward pressure stroke.

GOALS

Gently start applying pressure after rounding the top curve to create gradual increase in stroke width. The top of the curve should be a hairline. Aim for equal spacing, equal width, and slant that follows the guidelines.

x

x

x

x

x

x

x

x

COMPOUND CURVE

Start at the base line. Use no pressure on the upstroke transitioning to downward pressure stroke and back a to no pressure upstroke.

GOALS

Try to have gradual transitions from thick to thick lines. The top and bottom of the curves should be hairlines.

COMPOUND CURVE (REVERSE)

Start at mean line. Use pressure on the downstroke, transitioning to no pressure upstroke, and back to a pressure downstroke.

GOALS

Try to have gradual transitions from thick to thick lines. The bottom and top of the curves should be hairlines.

ASCENDING LOOP WITH ENTRANCE STROKE

Start at the baseline and use gently curving upstroke to the mean line. Lift nib and shift to right ever so slightly (the width of the down stroke) to begin upstroke again. Round the top at the ascending line and down.

GOALS

The top of the curve should be a hairline. Transitions from thick to thick should be gradual.

DESCENDING LOOP WITH EXIT STROKE

Start at the mean line and draw a downstroke. Round the curve clockwise into an upstroke. Upon meeting the base line, lift nib from paper and shift slightly to the right to "jump" the wet down stroke before adding a gently curving exit upstroke from the baseline to mean line (this avoids ink drag to keep line junctures crisp).

GOALS

The bottom of the curve should be a hairline. Transitions from thick to thick should be gradual.

OVAL

Start at the top drawing in a counter-clockwise direction gradually increasing then gradually decreasing the pressure.

GOALS

The top and bottom curves are both hairlines. The slant guides dissect the oval

PRACTICE
Use this space for additional practice at 6.5mm x height with 55° degree slant lines.

x

x

x

x

x

x

x

x

x

3.

Exemplar

A B C D E F G
H I J K L M N
O P Q R S T
U V W X Y Z
abcdefghijklmn
opqrstuvwxyz

4.

Minuscules

Let's make some actual letters!! The fabulous part about minuscules (lower case letters), is that almost every letter is formed by combining the basic strokes you just practiced. So, you can almost consider yourself a minuscule master before you even get started!!

You will notice that each page is dedicated to practicing a single minuscule. Look for the basic strokes that are combined to form each one. Again, we are trying to build those basic strokes into our muscle memory.

As you practice, be mindful of each stroke separately. The main difference between calligraphy and traditional cursive script is that we do not write in one continuous stream. Rather, we create letters by 'drawing' each stroke separately just as you did in the previous section. Lifting the pen slightly from the paper between each stroke also serves to "reset" your muscles. This gives you a chance to focus on one stroke at a time and makes all of this a tad bit easier.

You will also notice that the pages are not arranged in alphabetical order. When I teach calligraphy, I teach the minuscules in form-building order instead of alphabetically. But not to worry! They are all there.

At the top of the page, I have demonstrated the stroke breakdown and direction. Start each stroke at the open circle. After tracing multiple lines, you will trace a few and write independently.

Reminders:
- Move your paper to stay in your "writing zone"
- Dip between strokes after the eye "pops"
- Check the rotation of the holder in your hand
- Breathe

This section is at 6.5mm x-height with 55° degree slant lines.

Stroke 1   Stroke 2

dot: use circular motion,
make dot same width
as thick downstroke

start = ○
no pressure up
add pressure down
lift between strokes

Kestrel Montes: Minuscules

43

Stroke 1   Stroke 2

start = ○
no pressure up
add pressure down
lift between strokes

x

Stroke 1

start = ○
no pressure up
add pressure down
lift between strokes

Stroke 1   Stroke 2

start = ○
no pressure up
add pressure down
lift between strokes

x 𝑤ℓ 𝑤ℓ 𝑤ℓ 𝑤ℓ 𝑤ℓ 𝑤ℓ 𝑤ℓ 𝑤ℓ 𝑤ℓ 𝑤ℓ 𝑤ℓ

x 𝑤ℓ 𝑤ℓ 𝑤ℓ 𝑤ℓ 𝑤ℓ 𝑤ℓ 𝑤ℓ 𝑤ℓ 𝑤ℓ 𝑤ℓ 𝑤ℓ

x 𝑤ℓ 𝑤ℓ 𝑤ℓ 𝑤ℓ 𝑤ℓ 𝑤ℓ 𝑤ℓ 𝑤ℓ 𝑤ℓ 𝑤ℓ 𝑤ℓ

x 𝑤ℓ 𝑤ℓ 𝑤ℓ 𝑤ℓ 𝑤ℓ 𝑤ℓ 𝑤ℓ 𝑤ℓ 𝑤ℓ 𝑤ℓ 𝑤ℓ

x 𝑤ℓ 𝑤ℓ 𝑤ℓ 𝑤ℓ 𝑤ℓ 𝑤ℓ 𝑤ℓ 𝑤ℓ 𝑤ℓ 𝑤ℓ 𝑤ℓ

x 𝑤ℓ 𝑤ℓ 𝑤ℓ 𝑤ℓ 𝑤ℓ

x 𝑤ℓ 𝑤ℓ 𝑤ℓ 𝑤ℓ

x 𝑤ℓ 𝑤ℓ 𝑤ℓ 𝑤ℓ

x 𝑤ℓ 𝑤ℓ 𝑤ℓ 𝑤ℓ 𝑤ℓ

Stroke 1   Stroke 2

start = ∘
no pressure up
add pressure down
lift between strokes

x

x

x

x

x

x

x

x

Stroke 1 Stroke 2* * or use downstroke with no pressure

start = ○
no pressure up
add pressure down
lift between strokes

x

Stroke 1	Stroke 2

dot: use circular motion,
make dot same width
as thick downstroke

start = ○
no pressure up
add pressure down
lift between strokes

x *j* *j* *j* *j* *j* *j* *j* *j* *j* *j* *j* *j*

x *j* *j* *j* *j* *j* *j* *j* *j* *j* *j* *j* *j*

x *j* *j* *j* *j* *j* *j* *j* *j* *j* *j* *j* *j*

x *j* *j* *j* *j* *j* *j* *j* *j* *j* *j* *j* *j*

x *j* *j* *j* *j* *j* *j* *j* *j* *j* *j* *j* *j*

x *j* *j* *j* *j* *j*

x *j* *j* *j* *j* *j*

x *j* *j* *j* *j* *j*

x *j* *j* *j* *j* *j*

Stroke 1   Stroke 2

start = ∘
no pressure up
add pressure down
lift between strokes

x 𝓎 𝓎 𝓎 𝓎 𝓎 𝓎 𝓎 𝓎 𝓎 𝓎 𝓎

x 𝓎 𝓎 𝓎 𝓎 𝓎 𝓎 𝓎 𝓎 𝓎 𝓎 𝓎

x 𝓎 𝓎 𝓎 𝓎 𝓎 𝓎 𝓎 𝓎 𝓎 𝓎 𝓎

x 𝓎 𝓎 𝓎 𝓎 𝓎 𝓎 𝓎 𝓎 𝓎 𝓎 𝓎

x 𝓎 𝓎 𝓎 𝓎 𝓎 𝓎 𝓎 𝓎 𝓎 𝓎 𝓎

x 𝓎 𝓎 𝓎 𝓎 𝓎

x 𝓎 𝓎 𝓎 𝓎 𝓎

x 𝓎 𝓎 𝓎 𝓎 𝓎

x 𝓎 𝓎 𝓎 𝓎 𝓎

Stroke 1

start = ○
no pressure up
add pressure down
lift between strokes

x *C*

x *C*

x *C*

x *C*

x *C*

x *C*

x *C*

x *C*

x *C*

Stroke 1

x

Stroke 1

start = ○
no pressure up
add pressure down
lift between strokes

Stroke 1   Stroke 2

Stroke 1   Stroke 2

start = ○
no pressure up
add pressure down
lift between strokes

x 𝒢 𝒢 𝒢 𝒢 𝒢 𝒢 𝒢 𝒢 𝒢 𝒢

x 𝒢 𝒢 𝒢 𝒢 𝒢 𝒢 𝒢 𝒢 𝒢

x 𝒢 𝒢 𝒢 𝒢 𝒢 𝒢 𝒢 𝒢 𝒢

x 𝒢 𝒢 𝒢 𝒢 𝒢 𝒢 𝒢 𝒢 𝒢

x 𝒢 𝒢 𝒢 𝒢 𝒢 𝒢 𝒢 𝒢 𝒢

x 𝒢 𝒢 𝒢 𝒢 𝒢

x 𝒢 𝒢 𝒢 𝒢

x 𝒢 𝒢 𝒢 𝒢 𝒢

x 𝒢 𝒢 𝒢 𝒢 𝒢

Stroke 1   Stroke 2

start = ∘
no pressure up
add pressure down
lift between strokes

x *g*

x *g*

x *g*

x *g*

x *g*

x *g*

x *g*

x *g*

x *g*

Stroke 1

start = ○
no pressure up
add pressure down
lift between strokes

x   ℓ ℓ ℓ ℓ ℓ ℓ ℓ ℓ ℓ ℓ ℓ ℓ

x   ℓ ℓ ℓ ℓ ℓ ℓ ℓ ℓ ℓ ℓ ℓ ℓ

x   ℓ ℓ ℓ ℓ ℓ ℓ ℓ ℓ ℓ ℓ ℓ ℓ

x   ℓ ℓ ℓ ℓ ℓ ℓ ℓ ℓ ℓ ℓ ℓ ℓ

x   ℓ ℓ ℓ ℓ ℓ ℓ ℓ ℓ ℓ ℓ ℓ ℓ

x   ℓ ℓ ℓ ℓ ℓ ℓ

x   ℓ ℓ ℓ ℓ ℓ

x   ℓ ℓ ℓ ℓ ℓ

Stroke 1

Stroke 2

start = ∘
no pressure up
add pressure down
lift between strokes

x _d d d d d d d d d d d_

x _d d d d d d d d d d d_

x _d d d d d d d d d d d_

x _d d d d d d d d d d d_

x _d d d d d d d d d d d_

x _d d d d d_

x _d d d d d_

x _d d d d d_

x _d d d d d_

Stroke 1   Stroke 2

start = ○
no pressure up
add pressure down
lift between strokes

x

x

x

x

x

x

x

x

x

Stroke 1   Stroke 2

start = ∘
no pressure up
add pressure down
lift between strokes

x
x
x
x
x
x
x
x
x

Stroke 1*   * complete in one stroke

start = ∘
no pressure up
add pressure down
lift between strokes

Stroke 1

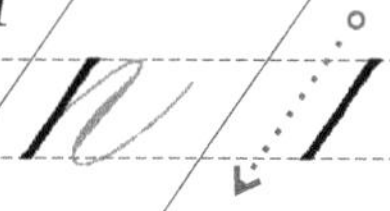

Stroke 2

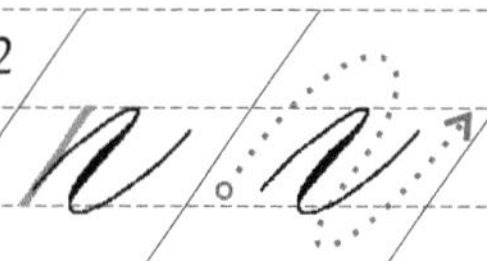

start = ○
no pressure up
add pressure down
lift between strokes

x

x

x

x

x

x

x

x

x

Stroke 1	Stroke 2	Stroke 3	start = ○
			no pressure up
			add pressure down
			lift between strokes

x 𝓂 𝓂 𝓂 𝓂 𝓂 𝓂 𝓂 𝓂 𝓂 𝓂

x 𝓂 𝓂 𝓂 𝓂 𝓂 𝓂 𝓂 𝓂 𝓂 𝓂

x 𝓂 𝓂 𝓂 𝓂 𝓂 𝓂 𝓂 𝓂 𝓂 𝓂

x 𝓂 𝓂 𝓂 𝓂 𝓂 𝓂 𝓂 𝓂 𝓂 𝓂

x 𝓂 𝓂 𝓂 𝓂 𝓂 𝓂 𝓂 𝓂 𝓂 𝓂

x 𝓂 𝓂 𝓂 𝓂 𝓂

x 𝓂 𝓂 𝓂 𝓂

x 𝓂 𝓂 𝓂 𝓂

x 𝓂 𝓂 𝓂 𝓂

Stroke 1

Stroke 2

start = ○
no pressure up
add pressure down
lift between strokes

x

x

x

x

x

x

x

x

x

Stroke 1

start = ∘
no pressure up
add pressure down
lift between strokes

Stroke 1

start = ○
no pressure up
add pressure down
lift between strokes

x

x

x

x

x

x

x

x

Stroke 1   Stroke 2

start = ○
no pressure up
add pressure down
lift between strokes

x

Stroke 1   Stroke 2

x

x

x

x

x

x

x

x

x

PRACTICE

Use this space for additional practice (6.5mm x height, 1:1:1, 55° degree slant lines).

x

x

x

x

x

x

x

x

x

6.5 mm, 1:1:1 relative x-height, 55 degrees

x

x

x

x

x

x

x

x

x

x

5.

Majuscules

You are rocking right along! Let's get you going with majuscules (upper case letters). Like with the minuscules chapter, each page is dedicated to practicing a single letter. However, these letters are in alphabetical order as they don't lend themselves as nicely to organization by shape.

Now that you have lots of practice, I want to challenge you in this chapter to focus on stroke pressure. Try to make your down strokes the same thickness (in other words, try not to have some letters more bold than others). This is achieved by applying the same amount of pressure to the pen each time. In calligraphy, our goal is consistency. The more consistent you are, the more polished your writing will appear.

Stroke pressure consistency takes a lot of practice and it takes mentally tuning into how your hand muscles feel as you write. Just pay attention to it but be nice to yourself if it's not quite happening yet. It will be our goal and, like all goals, they are not skills we have yet but rather skills we are striving for through practice and awareness.

I have demonstrated at the top of the page the stroke breakdown and direction. Start each stroke at the open circle. After tracing multiple lines, you will trace a few and write independently.

Reminders:
- Move your paper to stay in your "writing zone"
- Dip between strokes after the eye "pops"
- Check the rotation of the holder in your hand
- Breathe

This section is at 6.5mm x-height with 55° degree slant lines.

Stroke 1   Stroke 2

start = ○
no pressure up
add pressure down
lift between strokes

x   *G G G G G G G G G G G G G G*

x   *G G G G G G G G G G G G G G*

x   *G G G G G G G G G G G G G G*

x   *G G G G G G G G G G G G G G*

x   *G G G G G G G G G G G G G G*

x   *G G G G G*

x   *G G G G G*

x   *G G G G G*

x   *G G G G G*

Stroke 1* * complete in one stroke

start = ○
no pressure up
add pressure down
lift between strokes

x

Stroke 1

start = ∘
no pressure up
add pressure down
lift between strokes

x

x

x

x

x

x

x

x

Stroke 1* * complete in one stroke

start = ○
no pressure up
add pressure down
lift between strokes

Stroke 1* *complete in one stroke

start = ∘
no pressure up
add pressure down
lift between strokes

x

x

x

x

x

x

x

x

x

Stroke 1 Stroke 2

start = ∘
no pressure up
add pressure down
lift between strokes

x

Stroke 1   *Stroke 2*

start = ○
no pressure up
add pressure down
lift between strokes

x   *G G G G G G G G G G G*

x   *G G G G G G G G G G G*

x   *G G G G G G G G G G G*

x   *G G G G G G G G G G G*

x   *G G G G G G G G G G G*

x   *G G G G G*

x   *G G G G G*

x   *G G G G G*

x   *G G G G G*

Stroke 1   Stroke 2

x

x

x

x

x

x

x

x

x

Stroke 1

start = ○
no pressure up
add pressure down
lift between strokes

x

x

x

x

x

x

x

x

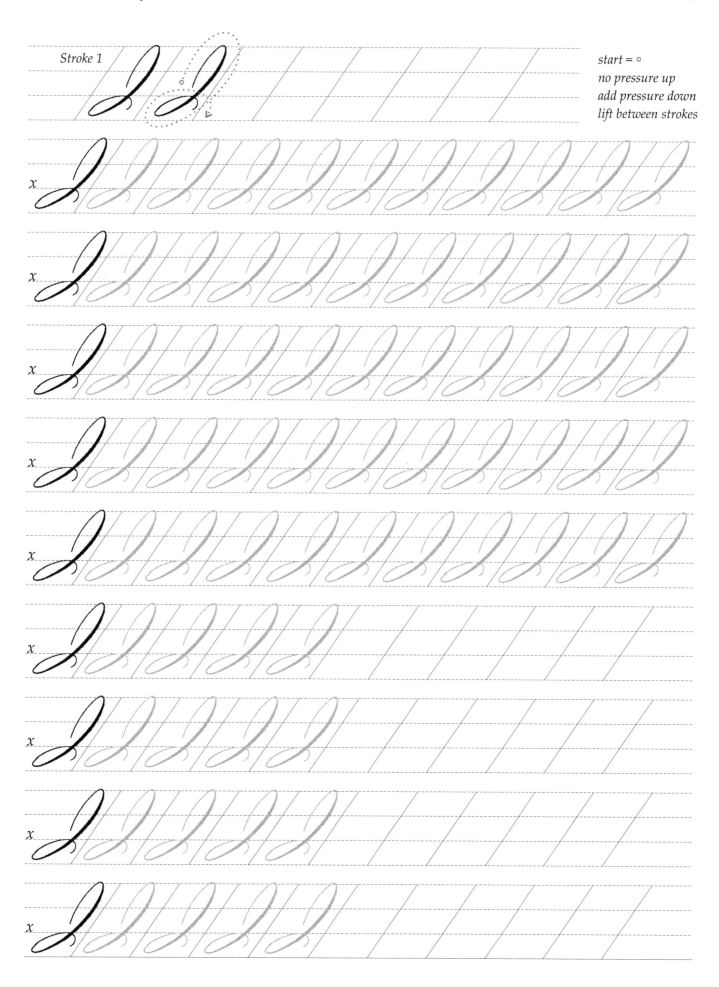

Stroke 1

start = ○
no pressure up
add pressure down
lift between strokes

x

x

x

x

x

x

x

x

Stroke 1   Stroke 2

start = ○
no pressure up
add pressure down
lift between strokes

x

Stroke 1

start = ○
no pressure up
add pressure down
lift between strokes

x *L*

x *L*

x *L*

x *L*

x *L*

x *L*

x *L*

x *L*

x *L*

Stroke 1

Stroke 2

start = ○
no pressure up
add pressure down
lift between strokes

x

x

x

x

x

x

x

x

Stroke 1

start = ○
no pressure up
add pressure down
lift between strokes

x

x

x

x

x

x

x

x

x

Stroke 1

start = ○
no pressure up
add pressure down
lift between strokes

x

x

x

x

x

x

x

x

Stroke 1

start = ○
no pressure up
add pressure down
lift between strokes

x

x

x

x

x

x

x

x

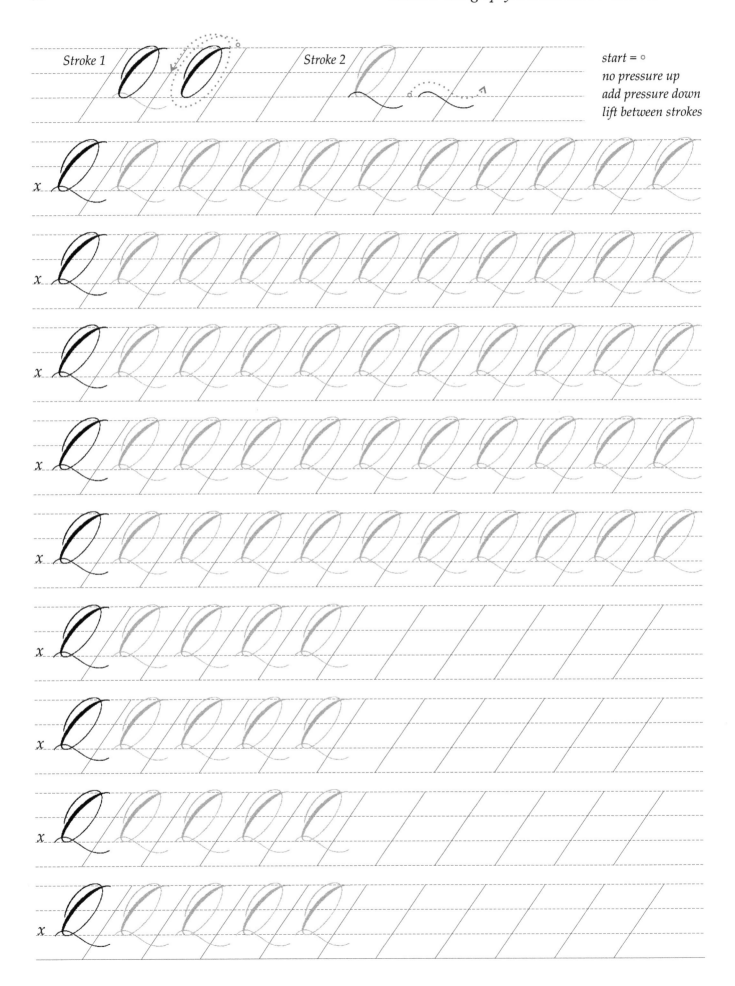

Stroke 1   Stroke 2   start = ○
                                                       no pressure up
                                                       add pressure down
                                                       lift between strokes

Stroke 1*   * complete in one stroke

start = ∘
no pressure up
add pressure down
lift between strokes

x

x

x

x

x

x

x

x

x

Stroke 1

start = ∘
no pressure up
add pressure down
lift between strokes

Stroke 1

start = ○
no pressure up
add pressure down
lift between strokes

x

x

x

x

x

x

x

x

Stroke 1   Stroke 2

start = ∘
no pressure up
add pressure down
lift between strokes

x

x

x

x

x

x

x

x

Stroke 1

start = ∘
no pressure up
add pressure down
lift between strokes

x

x

x

x

x

x

x

x

Stroke 1   Stroke 2

start = ∘
no pressure up
add pressure down
lift between strokes

x *W*

x *W*

x *W*

x *W*

x *W*

x *W*

x *W*

x *W*

x *W*

Stroke 1

Stroke 2

*or use downstroke
with no pressure

start = ○
no pressure up
add pressure down
lift between strokes

x

x

x

x

x

x

x

x

x

Stroke 1   Stroke 2

start = ∘
no pressure up
add pressure down
lift between strokes

x

x

x

x

x

x

x

x

x

Stroke 1*   *complete in one stroke   start = ○
                                                                                        no pressure up
                                                                                        add pressure down
                                                                                        lift between strokes

x

x

x

x

x

x

x

x

x

PRACTICE

Use this space for additional practice (6.5mm x height, 1:1:1, 55° degree slant lines).

x

x

x

x

x

x

x

x

x

x

x

x

x

x

x

x

x

x

x

6.

Numerals

Numbers! Such an important part of every envelope and escort card, and yet we often forget to practice numerals.

Numerals are typically larger than the x height. Notice that they extend about half way to the ascender line.

At the beginning of each line, I have demonstrated the stroke breakdown and direction. Start each stroke at the open circle. After tracing multiple shadows, you will write independently.

Reminders:
- Move your paper to stay in your "writing zone"
- Dip between strokes after the eye "pops"
- Check the rotation of the holder in your hand
- Breathe
- This is fun!!!

This section is at 6.5mm x-height with 55 ° degree slant lines.

x 1   1 1 1 1 1 1 1 1 1 1

x 2   2 2 2 2 2 2 2 2 2 2

x 3   3 3 3 3 3 3 3 3 3 3

x 4   4 4 4 4 4 4 4 4 4 4

x 5   5 5 5 5 5 5 5 5 5 5

x 6   6 6 6 6 6 6 6 6 6 6

x 7   7 7 7 7 7 7 7 7 7 7

x 8   8 8 8 8 8 8 8 8 8 8

x 9   9 9 9 9 9 9 9 9 9 9

x 0   0 0 0 0 0 0 0 0 0 0

x *1* 1 1 1 1 1

x *2* 2 2 2 2 2

x *3* 3 3 3 3 3

x *4* 4 4 4 4 4

x *5* 5 5 5 5 5

x *6* 6 6 6 6 6

x *7* 7 7 7 7 7

x *8* 8 8 8 8 8

x *9* 9 9 9 9 9

x *0* 0 0 0 0 0

7.

Connections

Now that you have mastered individual letters, let's put some together. Connecting letters is simply a matter of spacing our strokes such that the letters touch to form an appearance of a connected script. In most cases, the exit stroke of one letter becomes the entrance stroke of the following letter. That will be more clear as we dive in.

In this chapter, we will practice a few letter combinations as warm-up before jumping into whole words. I've included a selection of letter combinations that are common to the English language. At the top of each page, I have labeled the combination showing how I would break down the strokes using an open circle to show where I would start each new stroke. Note that in some cases, especially in combinations that include the letters r and s, the exit stroke from the proceeding letter will flow into the r/s as one continuous stroke. Not to worry! It's all about the practice!

Before writing with ink, try lightly tracing the example at the top without inking the nib. Use the blank space to try writing independently.

Reminders:
- Lift between each stroke
- Pay attention to how the letters connect
- You are on your way to writing gorgeous calligraphy!

This section is at 6.5mm x-height with 55° degree slant lines.

Stroke 1   Stroke 2   Stroke 3   start = ∘
                                                no pressure up
                                                add pressure down
                                                lift between strokes

x

x

x

x

Stroke 1   Stroke 2   Stroke 3

x

x

x

x

Stroke 1   Stroke 2   Stroke 3

start = ○
no pressure up
add pressure down
lift between strokes

x *ie* ie ie ie ie ie ie ie ie ie

x *ie* ie ie ie ie ie ie ie ie ie

x *ie* ie ie ie ie

x *ie* ie ie ie ie

Stroke 1   Stroke 2   Stroke 3   Stroke 4

x *ty* ty ty ty ty ty ty ty ty ty

x *ty* ty ty ty

x *ty* ty ty ty

x *ty* ty ty ty

Stroke 1	Stroke 2	Stroke 3	start = ∘

ou *ou* *ou*

start = ∘
no pressure up
add pressure down
lift between strokes

x *ou ou ou ou ou ou ou ou*

x *ou ou ou ou ou ou ou ou*

x *ou ou ou ou*

x *ou ou ou ou*

Stroke 1	Stroke 2*	Stroke 3	

th *th* *th*

* Normally, I cross the t at
the end of the word unless
I want to create a ligature
with the h.

x *th th th th th th th th*

x *th th th th th th th th*

x *th th th th*

x *th th th th*

Stroke 1   Stroke 2   Stroke 3

start = ○
no pressure up
add pressure down
lift between strokes

x _org_

x _org_

x _org_

x _org_

Stroke 1*   *Complete in one stroke

x

x

x

x

Stroke 1   Stroke 2   Stroke 3

start = ○
no pressure up
add pressure down
lift between strokes

x   *nos*   nos nos nos nos nos nos

x   *nos*   nos nos nos nos nos nos

x   *nos*   nos nos

x   *nos*   nos nos

Stroke 1   Stroke 2*   Stroke 3   Stroke 4

x   *ph*   ph ph ph ph ph ph

x   *ph*   ph ph ph ph ph ph

x   *ph*   ph ph

x   *ph*   ph ph

Stroke 1   *ert*   Stroke 2   *ert*   Stroke 3   *ert*

start = ○
no pressure up
add pressure down
lift between strokes

x   *ert ert ert ert ert ert*

x   *ert ert ert ert ert ert*

x   *ert ert ert*

x   *ert ert ert*

Stroke 1   *wh*   Stroke 2   *wh*   Stroke 3   *wh*   Stroke 4   *wh*

x   *wh wh wh wh wh wh wh wh*

x   *wh wh wh wh wh wh wh*

x   *wh wh wh*

x   *wh wh wh wh*

PRACTICE

Use this space for additional practice (6.5mm x height, 1:1:1, 55° degree slant lines).

x

x

x

x

x

x

x

x

x

x

x

x

x

x

x

x

x

x

x

8.
Whole Words

Let's put it all together!

Writing words is no different than writing individual letters. We are simply going to space the letters so that they touch each other. The spacing is what will give the appearance that everything is connected (but we are still going to lift instead of writing in a running script).

In this chapter, each page is dedicated to a single word. At the top of each page, I have labeled the word with how I would break down the strokes using an open circle to show where I would start each one.

Take a second to study the word first and dry trace the labeled word checking the stroke compilation. To help you determine directionality, remember that a thin line indicates an upward movement and a thick line would indicate a downward movement. After completing the whole word, return to dot any i/j and cross any t/x minuscules.

Trace each word and then use the last couple of lines to write independently.

Reminder:
* Lift between each stroke
* Make each stroke slowly and purposefully.
* Celebrate getting this far!

This section is at 6.5mm x-height with 55 ° degree slant lines.

○ = start new stroke

Gvenue / Gvenue

x

x Gvenue Gvenue Gvenue

x Gvenue Gvenue Gvenue

x Gvenue Gvenue Gvenue

x Gvenue Gvenue Gvenue

x Gvenue Gvenue Gvenue

x Gvenue Gvenue Gvenue

x Gvenue Gvenue Gvenue

x

x

x Beautiful Beautiful

○ = start new stroke

x Beautiful Beautiful

x Beautiful Beautiful

x Beautiful Beautiful

x Beautiful Beautiful

x Beautiful Beautiful

x Beautiful Beautiful

x Beautiful Beautiful

x

x

Crazier

○ = start new stroke

x

Crazier / *Crazier* /

x

Crazier / *Crazier* /

x

Crazier / *Crazier* /

x

Crazier / *Crazier* /

x

Crazier / *Crazier* /

x

Crazier / *Crazier* /

x

Crazier / *Crazier* /

x

x

○ = start new stroke

x *Dreams* Dreams Dreams Dreams

x Dreams Dreams Dreams

x Dreams Dreams Dreams

x Dreams Dreams Dreams

x Dreams Dreams Dreams

x Dreams Dreams Dreams

x Dreams Dreams Dreams

x Dreams Dreams Dreams

x

x

x *Event* / *Event* / ○ = start new stroke

x *Event* / *Event* / *Event* /

x *Event* / *Event* / *Event* /

x *Event* / *Event* / *Event* /

x *Event* / *Event* / *Event* /

x *Event* / *Event* / *Event* /

x *Event* / *Event* / *Event* /

x *Event* / *Event* / *Event* /

x

x

Flowers *Flowers* *Flowers*

x

Flowers *Flowers* *Flowers*

x

Flowers *Flowers* *Flowers*

x

Flowers *Flowers* *Flowers*

x

Flowers *Flowers* *Flowers*

x

Flowers *Flowers* *Flowers*

x

Flowers *Flowers* *Flowers*

x

Flowers *Flowers* *Flowers*

x

x

○ = start new stroke

x Guest Guest

x Guest Guest Guest

x Guest Guest Guest

x Guest Guest Guest

x Guest Guest Guest

x Guest Guest Guest

x Guest Guest Guest

x Guest Guest Guest

x

x

x Hotel Hotel

○ = start new stroke

x Hotel Hotel Hotel

x Hotel Hotel Hotel

x Hotel Hotel Hotel

x Hotel Hotel Hotel

x Hotel Hotel Hotel

x Hotel Hotel Hotel

x Hotel Hotel Hotel

x

x

Invited Invited

○ = start new stroke

x   Invited

x   Invited   Invited   Invited

x   Invited   Invited   Invited

x   Invited   Invited   Invited

x   Invited   Invited   Invited

x   Invited   Invited   Invited

x   Invited   Invited   Invited

x   Invited   Invited   Invited

x

x

x   *Juicy*   *Juicy*   ○ = start new stroke

x   *Juicy*   *Juicy*   *Juicy*

x   *Juicy*   *Juicy*   *Juicy*

x   *Juicy*   *Juicy*   *Juicy*

x   *Juicy*   *Juicy*   *Juicy*

x   *Juicy*   *Juicy*   *Juicy*

x   *Juicy*   *Juicy*   *Juicy*

x   *Juicy*   *Juicy*   *Juicy*

x

x

x *Kindly* Kindly

○ = start new stroke

x Kindly Kindly Kindly

x Kindly Kindly Kindly

x Kindly Kindly Kindly

x Kindly Kindly Kindly

x Kindly Kindly Kindly

x Kindly Kindly Kindly

x Kindly Kindly Kindly

x

x

x *Learning* *Learning*

x *Learning* *Learning*

x *Learning* *Learning*

x *Learning* *Learning*

x *Learning* *Learning*

x *Learning* *Learning*

x *Learning* *Learning*

x *Learning* *Learning*

x

x

Making   *Making*   *= start new stroke*

Making Making Making

Making Making Making

Making Making Making

Making Making Making

Making Making Making

Making Making Making

Making Making Making

November *November* ○ = start new stroke

November *November*

November *November*

November *November*

November *November*

November *November*

November *November*

November *November*

Opening   *Opening*   *Opening*

○ = start new stroke

x

Opening Opening Opening

x

Opening Opening Opening

x

Opening Opening Opening

x

Opening Opening Opening

x

Opening Opening Opening

x

Opening Opening Opening

x

Opening Opening Opening

x

x

x

Practice *Practice* *Practice*

○ = start new stroke

x

x *Practice* *Practice*

x *Practice* *Practice*

x *Practice* *Practice*

x *Practice* *Practice*

x *Practice* *Practice*

x *Practice* *Practice*

x *Practice* *Practice*

x

x

6 = start new stroke

x *Question* *Question*

x *Question* *Question* *Question*

x *Question* *Question* *Question*

x *Question* *Question* *Question*

x *Question* *Question* *Question*

x *Question* *Question* *Question*

x *Question* *Question* *Question*

x *Question* *Question* *Question*

x

x

○ = start new stroke

x *Request* Request

x Request Request Request

x Request Request Request

x Request Request Request

x Request Request Request

x Request Request Request

x Request Request Request

x Request Request Request

x

x

x Sincerely

○ = start new stroke

x Sincerely Sincerely

x Sincerely Sincerely

x Sincerely Sincerely

x Sincerely Sincerely

x Sincerely Sincerely

x Sincerely Sincerely

x Sincerely Sincerely

x

x

Thankful Thankful

○ = start new stroke

Thankful *Thankful*

Thankful *Thankful*

Thankful *Thankful*

Thankful *Thankful*

Thankful *Thankful*

Thankful *Thankful*

Thankful *Thankful*

Universal *Universal*

○ = start new stroke

x

Universal *Universal*

x

Universal *Universal*

x

Universal *Universal*

x

Universal *Universal*

x

Universal *Universal*

x

Universal *Universal*

x

Universal *Universal*

x

x

x

x *Vexing*

x *Vexing Vexing Vexing*

x *Vexing Vexing Vexing*

x *Vexing Vexing Vexing*

x *Vexing Vexing Vexing*

x *Vexing Vexing Vexing*

x *Vexing Vexing Vexing*

x *Vexing Vexing Vexing*

x

x

○ = *start new stroke*

Welcome *Welcome*

x

Welcome *Welcome*

x

Welcome *Welcome*

x

Welcome *Welcome*

x

Welcome *Welcome*

x

Welcome *Welcome*

x

Welcome *Welcome*

x

Welcome *Welcome*

x

x

x

x *Xerox* Xerox

x *Xerox* *Xerox* *Xerox*

x *Xerox* *Xerox* *Xerox*

x *Xerox* *Xerox* *Xerox*

x *Xerox* *Xerox* *Xerox*

x *Xerox* *Xerox* *Xerox*

x *Xerox* *Xerox* *Xerox*

x *Xerox* *Xerox* *Xerox*

x

x

○ = start new stroke

x   *Yesterday Yesterday*

x   *Yesterday Yesterday*

x   *Yesterday Yesterday*

x   *Yesterday Yesterday*

x   *Yesterday Yesterday*

x   *Yesterday Yesterday*

x   *Yesterday Yesterday*

x

x

x *Zigzag* *Zigzag*

○ = start new stroke

x *Zigzag* *Zigzag* *Zigzag*

x *Zigzag* *Zigzag* *Zigzag*

x *Zigzag* *Zigzag* *Zigzag*

x *Zigzag* *Zigzag* *Zigzag*

x *Zigzag* *Zigzag* *Zigzag*

x *Zigzag* *Zigzag* *Zigzag*

x *Zigzag* *Zigzag* *Zigzag*

x

x

PRACTICE
Use this space for additional practice (6.5mm x height, 1:1:1, 55° degree slant lines).

x

x

x

x

x

x

x

x

x

x

x

x

x

x

x

x

x

x

x

9.
Exrta Challenge

Ready for an extra challenge?

This chapter is full of quirky phrases that each contain all or most letters of the alphabet. In this section, I am taking the training wheels away and not even showing the stroke breakdown. You will be fine!!

You will also notice the condensed size of the lettering in this chapter. Many times we need to write smaller in order to fit our text in a given space. Place cards and envelopes don't offer us much real estate! This chapter gives you an opportunity to practice writing at a smaller size. You can also download free guide sheets from my website inkmethis.com to practice writing in other sizes.

Reminders:
- Move your paper to stay in your "writing zone"
- Dip between strokes after the eye "pops"
- Check the rotation of the holder in your hand
- Breathe
- This is fun!!!

This section is at 4.5mm x-height with 55° degree slant lines.

x The quick brown fox jumps over.

x The quick brown fox jumps over.

x The quick brown fox jumps over.

x

x The quick brown fox jumps over.

x

x The quick brown fox jumps over.

x

x The quick brown fox jumps over.

x

x The quick brown fox jumps over.

x

x The quick brown fox jumps over.

x

x *How quickly daft jumping zebras vex.*

x *How quickly daft jumping zebras vex.*

x *How quickly daft jumping zebras vex.*

x

x *How quickly daft jumping zebras vex.*

x

x *How quickly daft jumping zebras vex.*

x

x *How quickly daft jumping zebras vex.*

x

x *How quickly daft jumping zebras vex.*

x

x *How quickly daft jumping zebras vex.*

x

x *Two driven jocks help fax my big quiz.*

x *Two driven jocks help fax my big quiz.*

x *Two driven jocks help fax my big quiz.*

x

x *Two driven jocks help fax my big quiz.*

x

x *Two driven jocks help fax my big quiz.*

x

x *Two driven jocks help fax my big quiz.*

x

x *Two driven jocks help fax my big quiz.*

x

x *Two driven jocks help fax my big quiz.*

x

x Five quacking zephyrs jolt my wax bed.

x Five quacking zephyrs jolt my wax bed.

x Five quacking zephyrs jolt my wax bed.

x

x Five quacking zephyrs jolt my wax bed.

x

x Five quacking zephyrs jolt my wax bed.

x

x Five quacking zephyrs jolt my wax bed.

x

x Five quacking zephyrs jolt my wax bed.

x

x Five quacking zephyrs jolt my wax bed.

x

x   *The five boxing wizards jump quickly.*

x   The five boxing wizards jump quickly.

x   The five boxing wizards jump quickly.

x

x   The five boxing wizards jump quickly.

x

x   The five boxing wizards jump quickly.

x

x   The five boxing wizards jump quickly.

x

x   The five boxing wizards jump quickly.

x

x   The five boxing wizards jump quickly.

x

x Pack my bag with five dozen liquer jugs.

x Pack my bag with five dozen liquer jugs.

x Pack my bag with five dozen liquer jugs.

x

x Pack my bag with five dozen liquer jugs.

x

x Pack my bag with five dozen liquer jugs.

x

x Pack my bag with five dozen liquer jugs.

x

x Pack my bag with five dozen liquer jugs.

x

x Pack my bag with five dozen liquer jugs.

x

x Quick zephyrs blow, vexing daft Jim.

x Quick zephyrs blow, vexing daft Jim.

x Quick zephyrs blow, vexing daft Jim.

x

x Quick zephyrs blow, vexing daft Jim.

x

x Quick zephyrs blow, vexing daft Jim.

x

x Quick zephyrs blow, vexing daft Jim.

x

x Quick zephyrs blow, vexing daft Jim.

x

x Quick zephyrs blow, vexing daft Jim.

x

x Sphinx of black quartz judge my vow.

x Sphinx of black quartz judge my vow.

x Sphinx of black quartz judge my vow.

x

x Sphinx of black quartz judge my vow.

x

x Sphinx of black quartz judge my vow.

x

x Sphinx of black quartz judge my vow.

x

x Sphinx of black quartz judge my vow.

x

x Sphinx of black quartz judge my vow.

x

x Sympathizing would fix quicker objectives.

x Sympathizing would fix quicker objectives

x Sympathizing would fix quicker objectives

x

x Sympathizing would fix quicker objectives

x

x Sympathizing would fix quicker objectives

x

x Sympathizing would fix quicker objectives

x

x Sympathizing would fix quicker objectives

x

x Sympathizing would fix quicker objectives

x

x Many-wived Jack laughs at probe of sex quiz

x Many-wived Jack laughs at probe of sex quiz

x Many-wived Jack laughs at probe of sex quiz

x

x Many-wived Jack laughs at probe of sex quiz

x

x Many-wived Jack laughs at probe of sex quiz

x

x Many-wived Jack laughs at probe of sex quiz

x

x Many-wived Jack laughs at probe of sex quiz

x

x Many-wived Jack laughs at probe of sex quiz

x

x *Exquisite farm wench gave prize body jolt.*

x *Exquisite farm wench gave prize body jolt*

x *Exquisite farm wench gave prize body jolt*

x

x *Exquisite farm wench gave prize body jolt*

x

x *Exquisite farm wench gave prize body jolt*

x

x *Exquisite farm wench gave prize body jolt*

x

x *Exquisite farm wench gave prize body jolt*

x

x *Exquisite farm wench gave prize body jolt*

x

x *Gifted saxophones blew over Mike's quaff.*

x *Gifted saxophones blew over Mike's quaff.*

x *Gifted saxophones blew over Mike's quaff.*

x

x *Gifted saxophones blew over Mike's quaff.*

x

x *Gifted saxophones blew over Mike's quaff.*

x

x *Gifted saxophones blew over Mike's quaff.*

x

x *Gifted saxophones blew over Mike's quaff.*

x

x *Gifted saxophones blew over Mike's quaff.*

x

x A long fawn jumped over a white zink box.

x A long fawn jumped over a white zink box

x A long fawn jumped over a white zink box

x

x A long fawn jumped over a white zink box

x

x A long fawn jumped over a white zink box

x

x A long fawn jumped over a white zink box

x

x A long fawn jumped over a white zink box

x

x A long fawn jumped over a white zink box

x

x Playing quick vibe chords excites my wife.

x Playing quick vibe chords excites my wife

x Playing quick vibe chords excites my wife

x

x Playing quick vibe chords excites my wife

x

x Playing quick vibe chords excites my wife

x

x Playing quick vibe chords excites my wife

x

x Playing quick vibe chords excites my wife

x

x Playing quick vibe chords excites my wife

x

PRACTICE

Use this space for additional practice (4.5mm x height, 1:1:1, 55° degree slant lines).

x

x

x

x

x

x

x

x

x

x

x

x

x

x

x

x

x

x

x

x

x

x

x

x

ABOUT THE AUTHOR

Kestrel Montes lives in the Northern California wine country with her husband, Francisco. Together, they have five kids (Alex, Amanda, Oscar, Oliver, and Levi), a Yorkie, and an African Gray. Kestrel loves all things marble and gold. Francisco collects fun socks.

Kestrel and Francisco founded inkmethis in 2014, specializing in luxury calligraphy supplies, custom stamps, and engraved gifts. Francisco is an engraver and turns the beautiful calligraphy pen holders. Kestrel is a calligrapher and digital font designer. Formerly a career educator, Kestrel uses her pedagogical background to teach calligraphy and online business skills. Never actually setting out to be self-employed, they are incredibly thankful for the interest that has been shown in their work and products.

STAY IN TOUCH

Follow Kestrel on Instagram @inkmethis for calligraphy tips, website restocks and to see behind the scenes of the calligraphy business duo. Please share your calligraphy progress using the hashtag #learnwithkestrel for a chance to be reposted.

THANK YOU

Enjoy 10% off your next purchase from inkmethis.com with the code *learnwithkestrel* as a thank you for purchasing this book. On inkmethis.com, you will find luxury calligraphy supplies and gifts, custom stamps, digital fonts, and free calligraphy resources.

Photo: Charlie Couch

CPSIA information can be obtained
at www.ICGtesting.com
Printed in the USA
BVHW051704160919

558449BV00002BB/5/P